Amphibians
& Reptiles

naturally scottish

© Scottish Natural Heritage 2004

ISBN 1 85397 401 3 paperback

A CIPO record is held at the British Library

NP2.5K1204

Acknowledgements: Advice and comments from Martin Gaywood and Lynne Farrell (SNH)

Authors: John Buckley (HCT), Mairi Cole (SNH)

Series Editor: Lynne Farrell (SNH)

Design and production: SNH Design and Publications

Photographs: N. Benvie 22, 31; **L. Campbell** front cover right, back cover top, frontispiece, opposite 1 bottom, 6, 14 top left, 18, 21, 27, 36 top right, 36 bottom left; **S. Dalton/NHPA** 4 top, 4 bottom; **L. Gill/SNH** contents, 7, 11, 13 top, 19, 32, 33; **M. Hamblin** front cover top left, front cover bottom left, opposite 1 top, 10, 24, 36 centre left, 36 bottom right; **G. Logan** 36 top left; **J. Macpherson/SNH** 8; **MP/FLPA** 16; **R. Revels** 13 bottom; 14 bottom right; **N. Squirrell** 28; **P. Sterry** 14 top right, 17, 20, 23, 26; **J. Tulloch** 29; **D. Whitaker** 9; **M.B. Withers/FLPA** 14 bottom left.

Illustrations:
David Carstairs 30; **Clare Hewitt** 3; **Kelly Stuart** 5.

Scottish Natural Heritage
Design and Publications
Battleby
Redgorton
Perth PH1 3EW
Tel: 01738 458530
Fax: 01738 458613
E-mail: pubs@snh.gov.uk
www.snh.org.uk

Cover photographs:
Clockwise left to right:
Common toad *Bufo bufo*
Common lizard *Lacerta vivipara*
Common frog *Rana temporaria*

Frontispiece:
Scales of Common lizard
Lacerta vivipara

Back cover photograph:
Common frog tadpole
with front and hind legs

Amphibians & Reptiles

naturally scottish

by

John Buckley (The Herpetological Conservation Trust)

and

Mairi Cole (Scottish Natural Heritage)

Foreword

Amphibians and reptiles are surely amongst the most fascinating of all animals. As children, we become familiar at an early age with frogspawn and tadpoles, and wonder at their transformation into tiny frogs and toads. Further study of these creatures only adds to their intrigue. Toads regularly migrate great distances to reach their breeding ponds, and male adders "dance" together in competition for females in springtime. This beautifully illustrated booklet summarises the lifestyles of the six species of amphibians and four reptiles found in Scotland, and whets the appetite for personal encounters with them.

Scotland's northerly position in the British Isles, and relatively cool climate, sounds like bad news for cold-blooded animals such as amphibians and reptiles. However, the full complement of amphibians currently native to Britain can be found in Scotland. The three species of newts are reasonably widespread, though the great crested is rare in the northern half of the country. Common frogs and toads fare very well, generally better than in the more intensively farmed countryside that dominates much of England. Natterjacks, on the other hand, only just make it and are restricted to the southernmost region around the Solway coast. I still remember clearly the excitement of my first encounter with Scottish natterjacks during a national survey of the species in 1974. It is encouraging to note that since that time the natterjack has continued to thrive in Scotland, and even extended its range slightly, largely due to strenuous efforts by conservationists in the intervening years.

Heather-covered moorland, particularly south-facing slopes, makes for excellent reptile habitat. No doubt this is why adders, viviparous lizards and slow-worms thrive in many parts of the country. All three of these species give birth to live young, an advantageous strategy in cool summer weather. Females can move around and take every opportunity to bask in the sun, thereby accelerating the development of their young. This is probably why grass snakes, which lay eggs that may end up too cold to survive, are not resident in Scotland. Surprising, then, that egg-laying sand lizards have established themselves on a Hebridean island after introduction by man in the early 1970s. It turns out that summer sunshine hours in the Western Isles are similar to those in Merseyside, the natural northern range limit of sand lizards in Britain.

Hopefully this booklet will generate some new enthusiasts for frogs, toads, newts, lizards and snakes and increase their profile as important elements of Scotland's bountiful wildlife.

Trevor Beebee,
Professor of Molecular Ecology, University of Sussex

Pond at Tullo Farm, Aberdeenshire with sedges and rushes, an ideal place for amphibians and reptiles

Contents

Amphibians have soft, smooth skin, permeable to water. Amphibian eggs have no waterproof outer covering and have to be laid in water so amphibians must return there to breed before spending the rest of the year on land. The young aquatic stage of amphibians looks very different from the adult.

Common frog *Rana temporaria*

Common lizard *Lacerta vivipara*

Reptiles are covered with coarse, dry scales that are impervious to water. They have eggs with a waterproof covering which don't have to be laid in water. The young develop fully inside the egg and hatch out as miniature versions of the adult.

Introduction

Frogs, toads, newts, lizards and snakes are all familiar to most of us. They feature in folk lore and children's stories and, in countries with temperate climates, amphibians are still regarded as harbingers of spring. A chance encounter with them always arouses interest and sometimes strong feelings, from liking to loathing!

Approximately 350 million years ago, a fish ancestor developed limbs instead of fins and took the first steps towards life on land. This gave rise to a group of animals called tetrapods which eventually evolved into the amphibians. These successfully exploited the humid environment of the time around 340-320 million years ago. However, the landscape began to dry out, which led to further evolution of a new group of land-based reptiles approximately 300 million years ago. These became the dominant land animals in the Mesozoic era (approximately 200-70 million years ago). Although these groups have a common ancestor, they now represent very different types of animals with very different life strategies. Traditionally reptiles and amphibians have been studied together in the single discipline of herpetology, coined from the Greek word *herpeton* which means 'crawling thing'.

Amphibians and reptiles are very different to birds and mammals. They are ectotherms, which means that they make use of the sun's rays to heat their bodies until they are warm enough to be active. They do not use energy from their food to do this which means that they can survive in habitats where there is little to eat. As a result, individuals can live longer and, at a higher density than similar-sized mammals. But this dependency on the weather means that they cannot be properly active during long, cold periods so they hibernate in winter and are inactive at night in cooler parts of the world.

The lifestyle of these creatures is best suited to the Tropics where most of the world's 5,399 amphibian and 7,776 reptile species live. Europe is not so well endowed, especially northern Europe, and generally has fewer species than the south of the continent. Scotland has just nine native terrestrial species. Much remains to be found out about them and keen amateurs can still make a contribution to our understanding of these interesting animals by recording where they occur.

Amphibians lay their eggs in water. The young stages do not resemble the adult forms and spend much of their time in the water feeding and growing. As they grow they develop legs, lungs replace gills, and they metamorphose into minute versions of their parents. As with many animals, juvenile amphibians all resemble the female forms.

Amphibians have permeable skins so, on land, they have to avoid dehydration. They tend not to bask in the sun to raise their body temperature. Instead, they choose places which warm up sufficiently for them to become active, usually after dusk. Amphibians are easily found in the spring when they congregate at ponds to breed. They can then be seen during the daytime and, more easily, after dusk with the aid of a torch. All adult amphibians are carnivores; they feed on a variety of small creatures such as insects and worms.

There are two forms of amphibians in Scotland: frogs and toads (the 'Anurans' - without tails) and newts (the 'Urodeles' - with prominent tails). There is one species of frog (the Common frog *Rana temporaria*), two species of toads (the Common toad *Bufo bufo* and the Natterjack toad *Bufo calamita*) and three species of newts (the Smooth newt *Triturus vulgaris*, the Palmate newt *Triturus helveticus* and the Great crested, or warty, newt *Triturus cristatus*).

Diagram of pond showing the different depths that frogs, toads and newts prefer

Frogs and Toads

Frogs and toads belong to the world's largest group of amphibians, characterised by tail-less adults. They breed early in the year and the call of the males may get louder and more persistent as spawning approaches. During breeding the adult male holds on tightly to the female by clasping her round the chest with his front legs (in amplexus). This embrace can continue for several days or weeks until the female lays her eggs, at which point the male fertilizes them with his sperm. After being laid, the jelly coating surrounding the eggs absorbs water and swells up. All frogs in a pond tend to spawn at the same time, and mats of spawn can often be seen in the shallows of ponds. Frogs lay clumps of spawn whilst toads lay their spawn in strings.

The eggs eventually hatch into the familiar tadpoles. The tadpoles feed and grow, and develop hind legs before front ones. The speed of their development is controlled by factors such as the water temperature, the amount of food and the density of tadpoles in the pool. The tail is absorbed before they metamorphose and leave the pond.

Most of the animals seen at ponds are males waiting for females to arrive to breed. Females spend little time at the ponds and leave after spawning.

Top: Frog spawn with developing tadpoles
Below: Common toads in amplexus with their strings of spawn

4

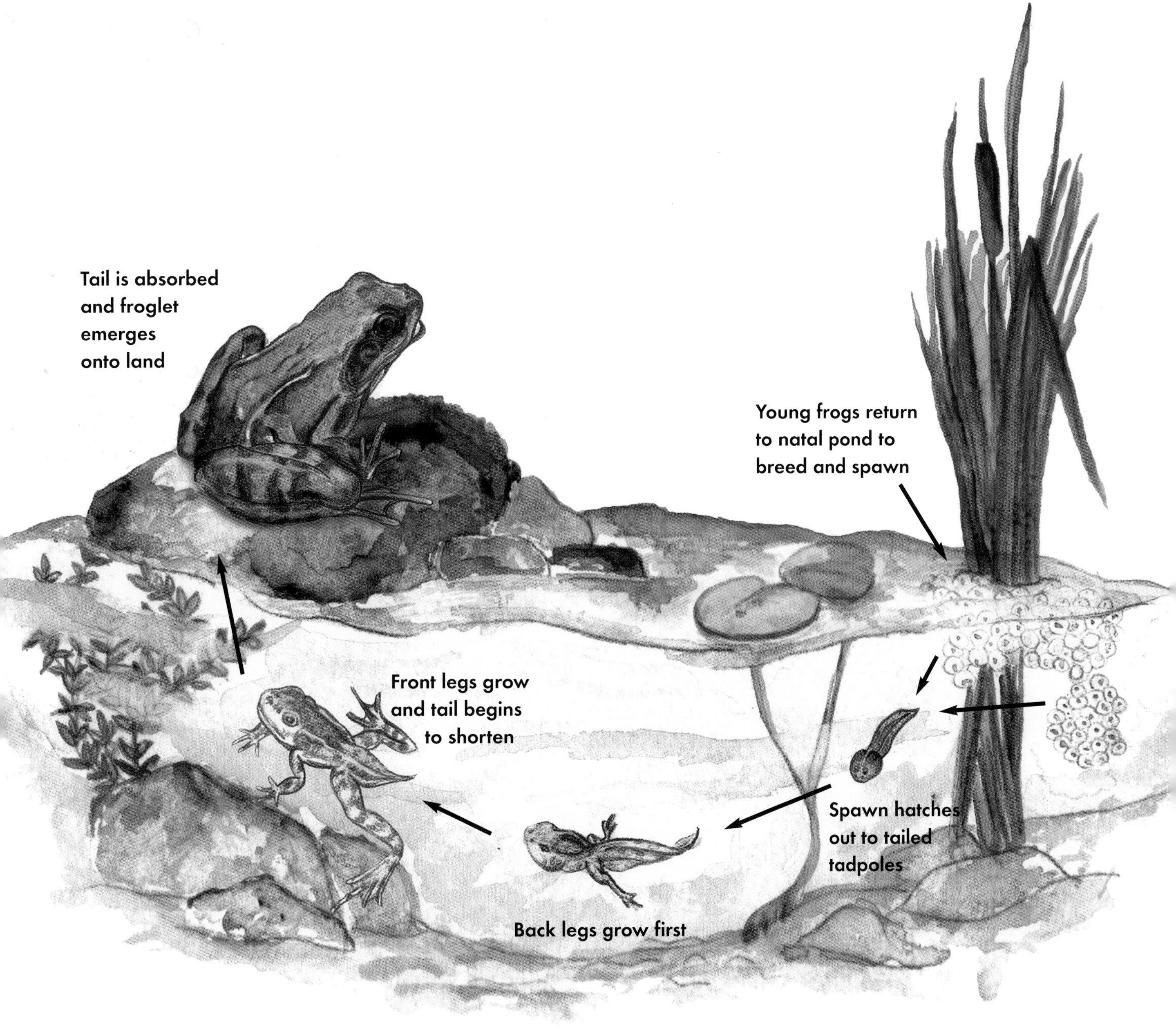

Tail is absorbed and froglet emerges onto land

Young frogs return to natal pond to breed and spawn

Front legs grow and tail begins to shorten

Spawn hatches out to tailed tadpoles

Back legs grow first

Lifecycle of a frog

Common frog Rana temporaria, sitting on Floating pondweed. The frog's eye is round and is a browny green colour.

Uath Lochan, Glenfeshie, Strathspey, a loch with shallow water at the margins and plenty of emerging plants

Common frog
Rana temporaria

Male Common frogs typically grow to a body length of about 6.5 centimetres and females up to 7 centimetres. The skin is relatively smooth and moist and the body has a distinct hump in the back. It is probably the most familiar amphibian in Britain but it can vary quite a lot in appearance. The background colour of the upper body is usually a shade of brown or grey, although yellow or russet individuals are often found. Individual frogs are marked to varying degrees with black or brown blotches or marbling. A dark patch covers the ear region and legs have dark bars across them. Males utter a low pitched croaking song.

The breeding season is March to April. The spawn is laid in clumps, like tapioca, in a great variety of still water bodies from tiny mountain pools to the shallow margins of large lowland lochs. Eggs and tadpoles are vulnerable to predation by fish and waterfowl. By the time they are half grown, the speckled, pale green or brown frog tadpoles are easily distinguished.

Frogs only feed on the land on mild, damp nights where they consume a variety of invertebrates including slugs, snails, beetles, caterpillars and spiders.

The Common frog is widespread and is found in suitable locations throughout Scotland, except in the most well-drained places. It also occurs on some of the islands of the Inner Hebrides and has been introduced to Shetland.

Rothiemurchus. Toads prefer deeper water with heathland and a drier area nearby

Common toad
Bufo bufo

Unlike the frog, the Common toad has a rough, warty skin. Females grow to a much larger size (13 centimetres) than males (8 centimetres). The colour is typically grey or brown, sometimes with irregular dark markings, and the eyes are an iridescent copper colour. Like the other amphibians, toads lighten or darken their skin according to environmental conditions. The Common toad is less agile than the frog and moves by crawling or hopping rather than jumping.

The breeding season is March to May, depending on the mildness of the weather, but is usually two to three weeks later than that of the frogs. The spawn is easily distinguished from frogspawn as it is laid in strings, not clumps. Toads seem to prefer ponds with fish and many hundreds of individuals may assemble to find mates and spawn in large, permanent water bodies. The tadpoles are jet black and the skin is poisonous to many potential predators. The Common toad is a 'sit and wait' predator, which snaps up invertebrates with its long tongue as they pass by. Ants, beetles, spiders and earwigs as well as worms, slugs and snails all feature in the diet.

The species is widespread in Scotland but the more specific habitat requirements makes it generally less common than the frog. Outside the breeding season, Common toads may travel hundreds of metres to localities with rough grassland, scrub or woodland where they can feed and hibernate in winter.

Common toad with its coppery-coloured eye and rough skin

Natterjack toad showing the distinctive yellow stripe. Natterjacks are not easy to see but their loud churr can often be heard at night

Natterjack toad
Bufo calamita

Male Natterjack toads may grow to nearly 7 centimetres long and females to a slightly larger size. These toads are easily recognised by their brown or olive-green skin with grey and reddish markings. A distinguishing yellow stripe runs down the centre of the back, and the eyes are yellow-green in colour and veined with black. The hind legs are relatively short so that they can run and crawl.

The Natterjack toad has always been restricted in its distribution in Britain but this has been reduced even more in Scotland over recent decades. Here, it is confined to sites along the north edge of the Solway Firth, in Dumfriesshire, where the toads live on merse, dune, heathland and the adjacent fields. There are now only five known colonies in this area.

Natterjack toads breed later than the Common frog and Common toad with mating occurring in May or June and sometimes even later. The males have a very loud call - a rasping churr - which attracts females. They have to find vacant pools as their tadpoles cannot compete successfully with other tadpoles and are vulnerable to predation by carnivorous invertebrates. Development in the warm, shallow breeding pools is rapid and the tadpoles soon metamorphose into miniature versions of the adults.

Natterjack toads are good burrowers and after dusk they leave their burrows to hunt prey over bare ground or short vegetation. They feed on beetles, ants, moths and other invertebrates.

The best way to hear and see Natterjacks in the springtime is to arrange a visit to a nature reserve such as Caerlaverock near Dumfries.

Habitat of Natterjack toads in Dumfriesshire

11

Newts

Scotland has three species of newt; the Smooth, the Palmate and the Great crested. Newts, and their cousins the Salamanders, are amphibians with long tails and elongated bodies. Their legs are short and both pairs are roughly the same size. On land, newts look superficially like lizards but can be distinguished by their scale-less skin. The males and females of all three species of newt are quite distinct (sexual dimorphism) and the juveniles resemble the females.

Breeding takes place in water. When they are ready to breed, males develop crests and bold tail markings to help their courtship displays. Their courtship display is quite impressive, with a male pursuing a female and displaying to her using a combination of body positions and tail movements to exhibit his marking to best effect. At the end of a successful display the male deposits a packet of sperm on the pond bottom and guides the female to pick it up. The eggs are fertilised inside her body and later a few hundred eggs are laid singly, usually wrapped in the leaf of a water plant. The eggs and larvae (the young stage of newts) of the Palmate and Smooth newts are indistinguishable from each other, but those of the Great crested newt are different, being much larger.

When they hatch, newt larvae have basically the same long body shape as the adults. They have feathery external gills behind which are rudimentary front limbs. They develop similarly to frog and toad tadpoles, for example developing limbs, losing the tail fin and re-absorbing the gills but, because they already resemble the adult shape, the metamorphosis is not so radical. They attach themselves to nearby vegetation and only become free-swimming when the mouth develops and they start to feed on small aquatic invertebrates. Young newts, known as efts, leave the pond then spend the next two or three years living on land as they mature.

Outside the breeding season newts live on land in the vicinity of the breeding ponds. Adults are relatively inactive at this time and spend much of the time in sheltered places, such as under logs or stones. They are not territorial and several individuals (adults and young) may be found together. They move to recesses below ground when the temperature drops to just above freezing in order to avoid frosts during hibernation.

An area of undisturbed terrestrial habitat with plenty of hiding places is very important for newts. A patchwork of rough grassland, scrub, and deciduous woodland extending around the breeding pond for several hundred metres is ideal.

Newts are best seen in ponds from March to June. As night falls they gather at the edge of the pond and can be easily watched with the help of a torch shone into the water. With care, courtship displays and egg-laying behaviour can be observed.

Newts are carnivorous and feed on land and in water, mainly on invertebrates, for example soil mites, springtails, worms, insects, spiders and slugs depending on the size of the newt. In the water they also eat freshwater shrimps and hog lice, as well as frog spawn and tadpoles. The larvae feed on smaller invertebrates like water fleas and insect larvae.

To some extent the loss of ponds in rural areas has been offset by the creation of garden ponds, which provide homes for these species.

Top: Newt eggs individually wrapped in water weed
Below: Good habitat for newts, a deep pond with plenty of surrounding plants and shaded areas

Palmate newt - female (top left) and male (top right)

Smooth newt - female (bottom left) and male (bottom right)

Palmate newt
Triturus helveticus

The Palmate newt is our smallest newt. It can grow up to 9 centimetres but is usually about 6 centimetres long. It gets it name from the palmated (webbed) hind feet of the breeding males. The colour of the topside of the body and tail is olive to yellowish-brown, and both sexes have a pale yellow belly with very few spots. The throat is pink or pale with no spots – which provides a good way of telling this species from the Smooth newt. During the breeding season, the male can be further recognised by its low, smooth crest and a filament extending from the end of its blunt tail.

The Palmate newt uses the slightly acidic ponds in soft water areas more readily than the other newts. It is often the only newt living in upland areas and is the most widespread and abundant newt in Scotland.

Smooth newt
Triturus vulgaris

The Smooth newt is slightly larger than the Palmate newt and may grow to a total length of 11 centimetres. Its smooth skin distinguishes it from the Great crested newt, which has a slightly granular skin. The upper body and tail are olive to yellowish-brown and the belly of both sexes is orange with black spots. The throat is whitish and almost always spotted by black dots that are smaller in the female. During the breeding season the male can be recognised by a crest which develops along the back and top of the tail, the upper edge of which is wavy along its length. The underside also deepens in colour at this time. The larvae, which are indistinguishable from those of the Palmate newt, spend most of their time concealed in areas of waterweeds where they hunt their food.

The Smooth newt is found throughout mainland Scotland but is more localised and less common than the Palmate. It prefers to breed in ponds with hard water and is most often found in lowland regions.

Great crested newt
Triturus cristatus

The Great crested newt is an impressive amphibian. It may grow to 16 centimetres long and is much bulkier than the other native newts. The upper body and tail are dark brown, often virtually black with fine white spots on the lower flank. The skin has very fine warts, which is why it is also known as the Warty newt.

In the breeding season, the male develops a jagged crest along the body to the base of the tail, and has a silvery stripe along the sides of the tail. The tail also develops a crest and the underside enlarges. The belly of both sexes is strikingly marked by irregular black blotches on a bright orange background. The eggs are about twice the size of Palmate or Smooth newts' eggs and are lighter in colour.

This newt is a lowland species whose distribution generally corresponds to hard water rather than soft water regions. Large, well-established ponds with plenty of weed-cover without fish are required. Unlike the larvae of the other newts, Great crested newt larvae hunt water fleas in open water, and are therefore more vulnerable to fish predation. In the water, adults eat a range of invertebrates as well as tadpoles and other newts.

The Great crested newt is rare in Scotland and about 100 breeding ponds are known, although new ones are frequently being discovered. Strongholds for this species are Dumfries and Galloway and the Central belt. There is also a cluster of populations in the Inverness area.

Female Great crested newt showing markings on belly

16

Great crested newt - male

Scotland has four terrestrial reptile species - the Adder, the Slow-worm, the Viviparous or Common lizard and the Sand lizard. The first three species are native, but the Sand lizard was introduced to a Hebridean island in the 1970s.

Reptiles have a more terrestrial lifestyle than amphibians, they bask in sunshine to reach the right body temperature to be fully active. They usually select open areas to do this, for example, on footpaths, and can be quite conspicuous. The best time to see reptiles is during dry and still conditions when the sun is out, especially in the mornings shortly after they emerge. However they may not be so visible on very hot days as they can get too warm if they stay in the direct sun too long.

A distinguishing feature of reptiles is their scaly skin, which they shed several times a year, in a process called sloughing or ecdysis. Snakes usually lose their skins in one piece and lizards often shed their skins in small pieces. Sloughs (shed skins) are a good way of detecting their presence in an area.

Reptiles mate in springtime and fertilisation is internal. Most of the world's species lay their eggs on land. This is not such a good strategy in cold climates and, instead, all of Scotland's native terrestrial reptiles bear live young. They keep their eggs inside their bodies so that when they bask, the eggs also become warm and develop quickly. Reptiles slow down in low temperatures, and usually hibernate between October and March. Since there is only a short time between giving birth in late summer and the onset of low temperature, the adults may not have enough time to get into breeding condition before winter and so may not breed every year.

Sloughed adder skin

18

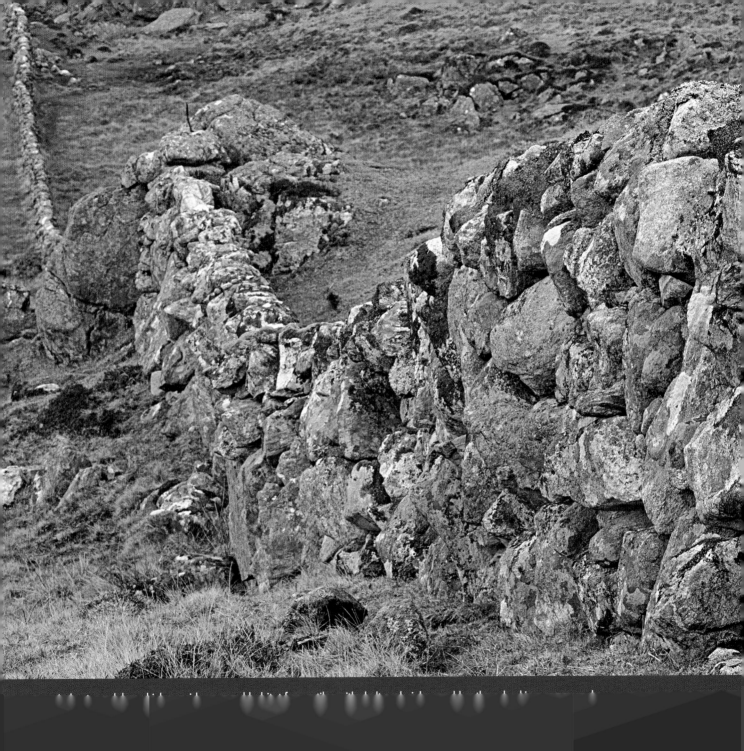

Snakes

Snakes are reptiles without moveable eyelids, external ear openings or limbs. They usually possess a deeply forked tongue and have rows of single scales which span the full width of the belly. Their flexible jaw structure can stretch enabling them to eat prey larger than their own heads. Only one species, the adder, is found in Scotland, although there are very occasional, unconfirmed reports of grass snakes in the far south of the country.

Adder showing distinctive patterning behind the head

Adder or Viper
Vipera berus

The Adder is a relatively short, stout snake. Females average about 65 centimetres and males are about 10 centimetres shorter. It is easily recognised by the dark zigzag pattern running along its back as well as a row of dark spots on each flank. On the top of the head there is usually a V, X or H - shaped dark mark. The sexes can often be distinguished by their background colour. Females are usually brown or reddish-brown and males grey or whitish. Females also tend to have a wider body and a distinctly narrower and shorter tail, in proportion to overall body length.

They are widespread but absent from much of the Central Lowlands, the Outer Hebrides and Northern Isles. Adders are found on heathland, moors, the borders of woods and fields, overgrown quarries and railway embankments. They tend to bask around sunny edges of dense ground vegetation, which provides a good source of warmth and deep cover, into which they can quickly escape when disturbed. They are absent from areas of intensive arable farming.

Adder in heathery moorland where it is most frequently found

Adders tend to have separate over-wintering and summer-feeding areas which can be hundreds of metres apart but linked by adder-friendly habitat. They hibernate in frost-free places below ground on thickly-vegetated, dry areas.

Voles and shrews are their main prey although their diet may also include lizards, young birds and occasionally frogs. Feeding has only rarely been observed in the wild. Adders probably combine active hunting with a 'sit-and-wait' strategy. When a snake strikes its prey, venom is injected and the snake recoils. It then follows the scent trail to the dying animal and consumes it once it is subdued.

After emerging from hibernation, the males shed their skin and start to look for females by following their scent trails. At this time, should a rival male be encountered a kind of wrestling match, called the dance of the adders, may ensue. The snakes entwine and try to force each other to the ground.

In cool climates the females only breed every other year at best, with the eggs developing inside the mother. Pregnant females return to hibernation areas and give birth to an average of nine young.

Adders are timid animals and snakebites are relatively uncommon in Britain. Most incidents involve the snakes defending themselves from being trodden on or picked up. If you see a snake, keep a reasonable distance from it, and do not attempt to touch or harm it. The snake is most likely to move away from you. Although snakebite symptoms can be painful and unpleasant, they are unlikely to be life-threatening. However, in all cases of snakebite the victim should be rested and reassured, whilst medical attention is sought as soon as possible.

Female adder basking on rock in an Angus glen

Male Common lizard warming up on a dry rocky surface, a typical habitat

Lizards

Lizards differ from snakes in a number of ways. They have eyelids and rows of small scales across their bellies rather than a single scale. When frightened they can shed part of their tail in an attempt to avoid being caught. The shed tail wiggles whilst the lizard makes its escape. Gradually a new end to the tail grows.

Common lizard
Lacerta vivipara

The Common lizard grows to a total length of about 13 – 15 centimetres, up to two-thirds of which is its tail. Adults are mainly brown, but may be yellowish, grey-reddish or greenish. The female has darker markings, a stripe down the back and a broad stripe down each flank. White lines often run parallel along the edges of the dark ones. The markings of the male are less distinct.

The Common lizard is an active hunter. The prey is seized in its mouth, shaken, chewed from end to end and then swallowed. It feeds on small invertebrates, particularly spiders and bugs.

Mating takes place in the spring after hibernation. Eggs develop inside the mother over three months during which time she basks to enable the embryos to develop and grow. She gives birth in late summer to six or seven young. The young are very dark brown, almost black.

In Scotland the Common lizard is widespread throughout the Highlands, Inner Hebrides and Southern Uplands but rare in the Central Lowlands and absent from the Northern Isles. Evidence suggests tt has declined in the Scottish lowlands as a result of intensive farming practices. It occupies a wide range of habitats, ideally south-facing to maximise exposure to the sun, and on well-drained soil. Short, dense vegetation, roadside verges, uncultivated field edges, forest rides and glades, cliff edges and scree slopes with open spaces provide good habitat. Lizards may also be found on artificial embankments, moors, heaths, coastal sand dunes and in suburban environments where there are few cats.

Often, a lizard is glimpsed or heard running from its basking place when it is disturbed. A better view can usually be obtained by waiting quietly for a few minutes, whilst it returns to its favourite spot.

Slow-worm
Anguis fragilis

The Slow-worm is often mistaken for a snake as it also has an elongated body. However it is a lizard without limbs and grows to a length of about 50 centimetres. The body colour is a shade of grey or brown. Females usually have a dark stripe down the back and dark sides to the body whilst males are uniform in colour. The tail and body are covered above and below with tiny scales which give the slow-worm a highly polished appearance.

Mating takes place in the spring and the young are born in late summer or early autumn. The average number in a clutch is about eight but it can vary from three to as many as 26 individuals. At birth Slow - worms are seven to ten centimetres long, golden-coloured with dark markings.

The majority of females only reproduce every other year, depending on environmental conditions. They can be a long-lived species, probably 15 years or more, in the wild. The Slow-worm is widely distributed in Scotland and found on all the larger, and many of the smaller islands off the west coast. It is the only reptile found on the Outer Hebrides. It can live in a variety of habitats including rough grassland, hedgerows, heathland, woodland edges and moorland. It also uses habitats influenced by human activity such as railway and road embankments, suburban gardens, churchyards and allotments. It eats mostly earthworms, slugs and snails.

Slow-worms rarely bask in the open and are most often encountered when turning over stones, wood, compost heaps, or scrap metal in suitable habitats, or when brought into homes by domestic cats.

Female Slow-worm showing its shiny appearance and dark stripe down its back

Sand Lizard
Lacerta agilis

The Sand lizard only occurs in Scotland as the result of an experimental introduction to the warm west coast. In 1971 thirty nine sand lizards from Dorset were released in an area of sand dunes on an Inner Hebridean island. The animals and their offspring have survived and bred in the area in which they were released.

The Sand lizard is bigger and more heavily built than the Common lizard and grows to a total length of 18-19 centimetres. The background skin colour is grey to pale brown. The sides of the body and back have a row of dark blotches with a central white dot or streak. During the breeding season the males' flanks become bright green. They are active hunters feeding on spiders, beetles, harvestmen, crickets and moths.

In Britain this species is confined to lowland heath and coastal sand dunes in a few parts of England.

Hibernation is followed by male rivalry, courtship and mating. The female lays her eggs in a burrow chosen from several she digs in soft sand. An average clutch is about five or six. The eggs hatch after seven to twelve weeks depending on temperature.

Other Species

There are other non-native reptiles and amphibians found in Scotland which have probably escaped from captivity, for example the Alpine newt found in ponds around Edinburgh.

The introduction of species to areas in which they do not occur naturally is not recommended as it can lead to problems ranging from competition with native species and spread of disease. They are also unlikely to survive in the longer term.

Marine turtles

There are also four species of marine turtle which are regularly seen in our coastal waters, the Leatherback turtle *Dermochelys coriacea*, the Loggerhead turtle *Caretta caretta*, Kemp's Ridley turtle *Lepidochelys kempii* and the Green turtle *Chelonia midas*. The latter three only turn up in Scotland as accidental vagrants and are usually in a poor state of health. The Leatherback, however, is a regular migratory visitor which comes to feed on the rich swarms of jellyfish off the west and north coasts of Scotland during late summer.

Leatherback turtle sighted off Shetland

Threats

Amphibians and reptiles are under threat from loss or fragmentation of their habitats. This is a particular problem in areas of urban development or where there are changes in agricultural practices. Species and sites can be protected by law against the human activities which cause habitat loss, but detrimental changes can also occur naturally. For example, too much shade resulting from the growth of trees makes ponds less suitable for amphibians and reptiles. The water becomes colder and there are fewer warm areas for basking.

Amphibians and reptiles are especially susceptible to atmospheric and water pollution. Frogs, with their porous skin, are very sensitive. Recent declines throughout the world indicate increasing levels of pollution.

In some parts of the world, frogs' legs are considered a delicacy, but this is hopefully not a dish that appears on the menu in many Scottish restaurants.

Conservation - how you can help

Pond management

Old and overgrown ponds can be restored and new ones created. Many ponds in the countryside have been drained, as areas that were previously used for grazing are now used for growing crops. Ponds and other water features on the village greens or near the edges of settlements have been in-filled as building has spread, or anxious parents fear for the safety of their children. But ponds are fascinating places where children of all ages can watch wildlife at close quarters if due care is taken. A pond in the garden is a welcome home to frogs, toads and newts. You will be surprised how quickly they take up residence, especially in an area where there are few other water bodies left. Advice on how to construct and maintain a pond is available from Pond Conservation.

Toads on the road campaign

In early spring, especially when the temperature starts to rise and there is a rainy night, frogs and toads begin to move to their traditional breeding grounds. If you go outside as darkness falls, you can often see them moving slowly across roads, both in the town and in the country. Many of these roads did not exist when the toads first used these sites, and now thousands of them are squashed by the increasing traffic. Several years ago the Toads on the Road campaign was initiated to help reduce the casualties. Volunteers are still needed in sensitive areas – Froglife can advise you where and when you can help. It can be fun wandering along the gutters with a torch and a bucket on a wet evening! There is a new road sign at the most frequently used toad crossings – be sure to slow down especially in March or April when the adults travel to the breeding areas, and also in July and August, when the young toadlets return to drier areas to feed, grow and later hibernate.

Collecting and rescuing frog spawn

Most children have collected at least one clump of frog spawn in their lives and kept it in a glass jar or tank to watch as it mysteriously developed into froglets. As many of the eggs do not reach maturity, either because they are eaten by other animals or are not fertile, or the water dries up, then removing a small part of a clump probably does not seriously deplete the overall resource and, of course, much is to be learnt from watching the development stages at close quarters. However, it is best to return the froglets near to the place from which the spawn was collected, to allow them to develop in their natural habitat.

If you see clumps of frogspawn left 'high and dry' by a prolonged dry spell of weather, then moving them gently to a nearby water body would be much appreciated – not least by the frogs themselves!

Collecting frogspawn

Recording schemes

Amphibians and reptiles are fortunately still common and widespread throughout most of Scotland, but with possible climatic changes and increased housing requirements, that may change. Everyone can help by noting down where and when they see amphibians and reptiles, and contributing to the national recording schemes.

Compost heaps and walls

Compost heaps provide a warm, relatively undisturbed, comfortable place in which reptiles in particular can sleep and hibernate. So turn over the compost heap carefully, especially in winter, and leave it until late Spring to spread the compost on the garden. Walls and rockeries are favoured hiding places for Slow-worms.

Non-use of pesticides and herbicides

Amphibians are susceptible to chemicals dissolved in water. Many of the chemicals used in both herbicides and pesticides are harmful to frogs, toads and newts, although the reptiles are less affected because of their impervious skins. Use of chemicals in the garden is not recommended if you want to see wildlife thriving, although many of the products are specifically targeted to kill so-called 'pest' species. Frogs and toads do help keep the garden tidy by eating slugs and other invertebrates.

Pond survey, searching for newts

Legal Protection

All amphibians and reptiles receive some protection under law in Scotland, although the degree of protection varies with the risk to the species.

The greatest protection is afforded to the Great crested newt, Natterjack toad, Sand lizard and all marine turtles. These are protected by The Conservation (Natural Heritage & C) Regulations 1994 and are known as European protected species. SNH should be consulted on any work, including surveys, involving either the species or the site on which these animals are known to live. A licence may be required to use certain methods of locating the animals during survey, for example using a torch may need a licence to 'disturb' the animals, but such surveys are important to provide current information on each of the species.

Scottish terrestrial reptile and amphibian species are protected under the Wildlife and Countryside Act 1981. It is illegal to intentionally kill or injure the Adder, Slow-worm or Common lizard. Licenses may be required for work involving sites which support these species if this work is likely to result in any killing or injuring. Again, SNH should be consulted on any work planned for areas supporting these species.

The four commoner species, Smooth newt, Palmate newt, Common frog and Common toad, are protected against sale, transporting for sale or advertising for sale. It is not an offence to handle or take these animals.

The Biodiversity Action Plan

The Natterjack toad and the Great crested newt are species listed on the UK Biodiversity Action Plan and both have Action Plans for the areas in which they occur in Scotland.

All of the marine turtles and the Sand lizard are included in the UK BAP.

34

Male Natterjack toad calling

Ancient symbols

Reptiles in particular had a significance in historical times, and a snake or serpent appears on Pictish stones. They represented wisdom and healing, renewal and immortality.

Scottish names:

Amphibians:

Frog: puddock, paddock, poddock, paddy

Frogspawn: paddy ladle, crud, puddock's gener, puddock's redd

Tadpole: ladle, kail-ladle, puddock's pony, powheid, pollywag, powrit, pallet, powag, beetleheid

Toad: corby, gangrell, taid, yird taid

In Orkney toads were called huppous and were believed to sit on the wheatears' eggs to hatch them.

Newt: ask, esk, man-keeper

Reptiles:

Adder: ether, edder, nether, neddyr

Lizard: dirdy-lochrag, dirdy-wachlag, lesart,

Slow-worm: slae

Standing stone at Logierait, Perthshire, showing a serpent

Finding out more about amphibians and reptiles

Beebee, T.J.C. and Griffiths, R.A. 2000. *Amphibians and Reptiles: A Natural History of the British Herpetofauna*. HarperCollins Publishers, London.

Bardsley, L. 2003. *The Wildlife Pond Handbook*. New Holland Publishers (UK).

Beebee, T.J.C. 1985. *Frogs and Toads*. Whittet Books, London.

Langton, T. 1989. *Snakes and Lizards*. Whittet Books, London.

Langton, T., Beckett, C. and Foster, J. 2001. *Great Crested Newt conservation handbook*. Froglife, Halesworth

Slater, F. 1992. *The Common Toad*. Shire Natural History Series No. 60.

Stafford, P. 1987. *The Adder*. Shire Natural History Series No. 18.

Stafford, P. 1989. *Lizards of the British Isles*. Shire Natural History Series No. 46.

Sterry, P. 1997. *Complete British Wildlife Photoguide*. HarperCollins Publishers, London.

Useful Addresses/Contacts

Biological Recording in Scotland (BRISC)
www.brisc.org.uk

Froglife (local contacts in Badenoch and Strathspey, Clyde, Fife, Gordon, Kincardine and Deeside, and Lothian)
White Lodge, London Road, Peterborough PE7 OLG
01733 558848
www.froglife.org

The Herpetological Conservation Trust
655a Christchurch Road, Boscombe
Bournemouth BH1 4AP
01202 391319   www.herpconstrust.org.uk

Kindrogan Field Centre, Field Studies Council, Enochdu, Blairgowrie, Perthshire PH10 7PG
E-mail: kindrogan@btinternet.com
www.econet.org.uk/kindrogan

Pond Conservation,
BMS, Oxford Brookes University, Gipsy Lane, Headington, Oxford OX3 0BP
01865 483249   www.pondstrust.org.uk

The UK Biodiversity Action Plan
www.ukbap.org.uk

Also in the Naturally Scottish series...

If you have enjoyed Lichens why not find out more about Scotland's wildlife in our Naturally Scottish series. Each booklet looks at one or more of Scotland's native species. The clear and informative text is illustrated with exceptional photographs by top wildlife photographers, showing the species in their native habitats and illustrating their relationships with man. They also provide information on conservation and the law.

Badgers

With its distinctive black and white striped face and short, squat body, the badger is probably one of the most popular mammals in Britain. Packed with stunning photographs, this publication reveals some amazing facts about the shy, secretive badger.
Mairi Cooper & John Ralston
ISBN 1 85397 254 1 pbk 16pp £3.00

Bumblebees

Did you know that Bummiebee, Droner and Foggie-toddler are all Scottish names for the bumblebee? Find out what these names mean and why bumblebees are so special inside this beautifully illustrated booklet. Also discover how you can help the bumblebee by planting appropriate flowers for their continued survival.
Murdo Macdonald
ISBN 1 85397 364 5 pbk 40pp £4.95

Burnet Moths

Unlike many other species of moth, burnet moths fly by day. They can be easily recognised by their beautiful, glossy black wings with crimson spots. Their striking colouring is a very real warning to predators.
Mark Young
ISBN 1 85397 209 6 pbk 24pp £3.00

Corncrakes

Secretive, skulking, rasping, loud, tuneless, scarce. . . all these words have been used to describe the corncrake. But once you could have added plentiful and widespread to the list. Now only a few birds visit Scotland each year. This booklet brings you the latest information on the corncrake and reveals this elusive and noisy bird in its grassy home.
Helen Riley, Rhys Green
ISBN 1 85397 049 2 pbk 40pp £3.95

Fungi

Fungi belong to one of the most varied, useful and ancient kingdoms in the natural world. Scotland may have almost 2000 larger species with some of the most interesting found in our woodlands and grasslands. This booklet provides an introduction to their life cycles, habitats and conservation. Discover the fascinating forms of earthstars, truffles and waxcaps.
Roy Watling MBE and Stephen Ward
ISBN 1 85397 341 6 pbk 40pp £4.95

Lichens

There are more than 1700 species of lichen occurring throughout the British Isles, and many grow in Scotland where the air is purer. Several different species may be found on a single rock or tree, resulting in lichenologists spending hours in one spot!
Oliver Gilbert
ISBN 1 85397 373 4 pbk 52pp £4.95

Red Kites

This graceful and distinctive bird was absent from Scotland's skies for more than a century. Now with the help of a successful programme of re-introduction, it's russet plumage and forked tail can once again be seen in Scotland.
David Minns and Doug Gilbert
ISBN 1 85397 210 X pbk 24pp £3.95

Red Squirrels

The red squirrel is one Scotland's most endearing mammals. This booklet provides an insight into their ecology and some of the problems facing red squirrels in Scotland today.
Peter Lurz & Mairi Cooper
ISBN 1 85397 298 4 pbk 20pp £3.00

River Runners

Scotland's clean, cascading rivers contain a fascinating array of species. The atlantic salmon is the best known of our riverine species but others, such as lampreys and freshwater pearl mussels, are frequently overlooked but no less captivating. This booklet aims to illuminate aspects of their intriguing and largely unseen lifecycles, habitats and conservation measures
Iain Sime
ISBN 1 85397 353 X pbk 44pp £4.95

Sea Eagles

This magnificent bird, with its wing span of over 2m is the largest bird of prey in Britain. In 1916 they became extinct, but a reintroduction programme began in 1975. This booklet documents the return of this truly majestic eagle. Production subsidised by Anheuser-Busch.
Greg Mudge, Kevin Duffy, Kate Thompson & John Love
ISBN 1 85397 208 8 pbk 16pp £1.50

SNH Publications Order Form:
Naturally Scottish Series

Title	Price	Quantity
Amphibians & Reptiles	£4.95	
Badgers	£3.00	
Bumblebees	£4.95	
Burnet Moths	£3.00	
Corncrakes	£3.95	
Fungi	£4.95	
Lichens	£4.95	
Red Kites	£3.95	
Red Squirrels	£3.00	
River Runners	£4.95	
Sea Eagles	£1.50	

Postage and packing: free of charge in the UK, a standard charge of £2.95 will be applied to all orders from the European Union. Elsewhere a standard charge of £5.50 will be applied for postage.

Please complete in BLOCK CAPITALS

Name _____

Address _____

_____

_____

Post Code

Type of Credit Card   VISA ☐   MasterCard ☐

Name of card holder _____

Card Number
☐☐☐☐ ☐☐☐☐ ☐☐☐☐ ☐☐☐☐

Expiry Date ☐☐ ☐☐

Send order and cheque made payable to Scottish Natural Heritage to:

Scottish Natural Heritage. Design and Publications, Battleby, Redgorton, Perth PH1 3EW

pubs@redgore.demon.co.uk

www.snh.org.uk

Please add my name to the mailing list for the: SNH Magazine ☐

Publications Catalogue ☐